All about my grandfather

My grandfather is old now. I visit him often and we get on well. He is my father's father and is eighty-four years old. To me he has always been old. I never knew him when he was young. But of course, he has told me about his life.

My grandfather was born at the end of the first world war. His father was a soldier in the war. When the war ended, my grandfather's parents were glad to be able to settle back into a normal life and start a family. My grandfather was one of the four children— two girls and two boys.

When they were growing up, there were many open spaces in their town. And so, my grandfather, his brother, his sisters and their friends found lots of places to play and to make huts. They also climbed trees. Those were the days long before computers and television. Children in that time had fun.

At that time, the war had left many families poor and sometimes there wasn't enough food. The schools tried to help by making sure that each child received a small bottle of milk each day to drink.

In the evenings, the children would sit down
and listen to the adventure stories and music on
the radio.

The trouble with dinosaurs

This book belongs to

_____

Written by Stephen Barnett
Illustrated by Rosie Brooks

Contents

About this book

A story about a grandfather and another about keeping dinosaurs as pets bring interest to confident readers looking for new ideas and vocabulary. A list of the new words and questions based on the stories enhance the reading experience.

When my grandfather left school, he became a train engineer. Then, he became a train driver on the long-distance trains that ran back and forth across the country. Although there were passenger planes, these were expensive. So most people on business or a holiday travelled by trains.

My grandmother, looked after the family and did some part-time work in the local library. She knitted most of the children's winter pullovers and scarves.

When my grandfather wasn't driving trains, he would spend time in his garden growing vegetables and fixing things out in the shed. He and my grandmother were members of the local tennis club. So in the summer, they would go on Saturday afternoons to play. My grandfather made sure that he taught his children how to play tennis as well, and my father taught me and my brothers. Tennis is a tradition in our family.

When my grandfather turned 65, he had to retire from the railways. After so many years he was happy to take a break from work, but for a while he missed his work friends. He also missed driving his train through the countryside and seeing the changing seasons.

But retirement for my grandfather didn't mean that he was going to sit around in a chair all day. Oh no! Pretty soon grandfather and my grandmother had joined a few clubs to keep themselves busy. Grandfather would also often come across to our house and help dad with things that needed to be done like digging the vegetable garden, and repairing the broken toys. He was always doing something.

As grandfather got older, he stopped doing all of the things he once had energy for, and started to relax more. He had always enjoyed reading and now in the afternoons after a busy morning he is found sitting outside in a chair and reading his latest book. He often says to me, 'Jonathan, one of the great joys in life is sitting in the sunshine and not doing much at all!' And then he laughs.

Sometimes on weekends I visit him and we play
a game of chess or he reads while I weed his
vegetable garden. He sits in the sun and dozes
or he gets up and goes inside to make a cup of
tea for us and my grandmother.

My grandfather had a good life and he will continue to enjoy it right until the end.

The trouble with dinosaurs

The big trouble with having a dinosaur as a pet is the space it takes up.

For example, our first dinosaur was a baby Stegosaurus. The people at the shop we bought it from assured us that it wouldn't grow much bigger than a television set.

Well, that's not what happened. 'Stego', as we called the dinosaur, was that big within a month and she kept on growing! Have you ever tried to get a teenage Stegosaurus off the sofa when you wanted to sit there?

Many dinosaurs are so big that their bodies need lots and lots of food. They spend most of the day eating.

Stego ate only vegetables. So that wasn't so bad. We could take her to a park and she would spend the day happily munching on trees and grass.

With meat-eating dinosaurs, you really
have problems. For a while we also had a
Velociraptor dinosaur. He was named 'Ripper'.

Ripper was small as well when we got him.
For a while it was fun to watch him race about
chasing mice and small insects for his meals.
But then he started to grow.

We fed Ripper six tins of dog food each day. But still various pets in the neighbourhood like cats, dogs, guinea pigs started to go missing. Within a month there was hardly a dog or a cat to be seen. We never saw Ripper actually eating one of the neighbours' pets, but I think it must have been him.

We took Stego and Ripper back to the pet shop and looked for something in the dinosaur line that would be less trouble. My sister spotted some white dinosaur eggs under a warming light. The eggs were not large and we thought that they would not be of much trouble even after hatching.

When the egg hatched, out came a small Pterosaur. It didn't look as though it was going to be very big. And moreover, it would be great fun to watch it fly around the house when it would grow up.

We were wrong. 'Terry' quickly grew to the size of a hang-glider. And she liked fish. In the next door house there was a pond in the garden with goldfish in it. But not for long. Terry would swoop down low over the pond and scoop up the fish. The neighbours weren't very happy.

Dinosaurs are just too big!

These days we have a dog and a cat. They're fun, and they don't take up so much room. But now and then we miss Stego, Ripper and Terry. But not too much!

New words

adventure	happy	Saturday
afternoon	hatch	scarves
bottle	hut	scoop
business	imagine	season
busy	knit	second
chair	latest	size
change	library	sofa
chess	local	soldier
computer	member	Stegosaurus
continue	mice	summer
country	munching	teenage
dig	normal	television
dinosaur	paint	tennis club
driver	part-time work	town
energy	passenger plane	toy
enjoy	perch	train engineer
expensive	pet	travel
fish	pond	vegetable
fix	pullover	Velociraptor
fruit	radio	winter
grandfather	read	world war
grandmother	relax	
grow	repair	
hang-glider	retire	

What did you learn?

All about my grandfather

What work did the grandfather do?

What sport did the grandfather play?

What game do the grandfather and Jonathan play?

The trouble with dinosaurs

What kind of dinosaur did the family have first?

What were the names of the dinosaurs?

What animals do the children have now?